Unique Animals and Birds of Australia

Rigby

The elegant Black Swan, Western Australia's State emblem, is Australia's only native swan and its trumpeting call echoes hauntingly over waterways throughout the continent. Until its discovery all swans were thought to be white.

1 Wildlife in an Ancient Land

The fauna of the Australian region has been shaped, to a large degree, by isolation. The continent has been separated from any other land mass for at least sixty million years, a situation which has had important consequences. Firstly, it has allowed some of Nature's most primitive creatures to survive in Australia long after they have disappeared from other regions of the world. Secondly, it has enabled significant groups of animals, such as the marsupials, to flourish and extend with little interference — protected from migratory predators or excessive competition between species.

The characteristics and habits of the native fauna have also been governed by the need to adapt to the environment. This is a flat continent lacking any major mountain ranges, and an arid one. Here there are few extensive areas of grazing land rich enough to support herds of large animals like buffaloes or deer. Instead, adaptation to dry conditions is a notable feature of nearly all categories of the native fauna. Large meat-eaters like the northern hemisphere bears or the lions and other big cats of Africa, are absent; the Australian fauna is largely herbivorous, feeding on grasses or the leaves, seeds and flowers of native vegetation. The breeding activity of many birds, for example, is associated with or subject to rainfall; fewer young are reared in dry seasons than when the rains have been good. Most native mammals, reptiles and birds have the ability to go for long periods without water; some never drink, obtaining the moisture they need to survive from their diet. Many groups of animals, notably the marsupials, are more or less nocturnal creatures, that is, active only during the night or at dawn or dusk when the sun is low and the air temperature moderate.

The Australian fauna is also notable in that it contains important groups of animals which are either sparsely represented or not found at all in other regions of the world. Here, too, we find groups of animals which, through their isolation, have developed quite differently over millions of years from their biological relatives in the northern hemisphere.

The monotremes are an example of the former category. Their sole representatives, the Australian platypus and echidna, are the last survivors of an ancient and primitive class of animals. 'Animal' to the layman generally means a placental mammal — a warm-blooded creature which gives birth to its young in a fully-formed condition and suckles it in its

5

infancy. The monotremes, however, are a very special sub-class of the mammals: the female lays eggs, in the manner of reptiles, but after incubation and hatching suckles the young in the mammalian fashion. They are 'primitive' creatures on the evolutionary scale, the word 'monotreme' being a reference to the fact that, like reptiles, monotremes possess a single body opening (the cloaca) which is used for both reproduction and the excretion of wastes. Some scientists regard the ancestors of the monotremes as a stage in the evolution of mammals from reptiles.

The other important group among the native fauna contains the marsupials, and includes such well-known animals as the kangaroos and possums, the Wombat and the Koala. Marsupials belong to a sub-class of the mammals and are distinguished from the other mammals by the fact that the young are not fully formed at birth. Instead the offspring are born in a semi-developed state and complete their early development in a pouch (marsupium) which has an opening on the external surface of the female's body and serves as a kind of womb substitute. The young of the Red Kangaroo, for instance, is scarcely larger than a bean when it is born.

The marsupials are the dominant group in Australia's furred fauna, comprising almost half of the 230 species of native mammals. Once they flourished in the northern hemisphere from Europe to North America but today the only other marsupials are the opossums and their relatives in North, South and Central America.

The other Australian mammals — the placentals — give birth to their young full-formed in the 'conventional' way. The best-known example is probably the Dingo, the native dog descended from the ancestors of the domestic dog. Two other native non-marsupial groups are the rodents — comprising about 70 species of rats, water rats and mice — and the Australian bats, which comprise about ten species of fruit bats or flying foxes, and about 40 species of insectivorous bats. The remaining placental mammals are marine creatures: whales, seals, dolphins and the seal-like Dugong.

The bird life of Australia is abundant; in proportion to area there are twice as many species as in North America and there is more variety among the birds than in almost any other group of native fauna. Since the movements of birds are not restricted in the same way as ground-dwelling creatures, the isolation of the continent has not had the influence on Australia's avifauna that it has had on its mammals. There is considerable 'overlap' between species found here and in the northern islands and southern Asia.

Roughly 750 species of birds are found in the continent, plus introduced species and migrants such as seabirds. Of this number about 500 are land-dwelling birds, and some 350 of these belong to the order of passerines or perching song-birds. In this order we find almost 70 species of honeyeaters and many small, colourful songsters such as robins, fantails, flycatchers, finches and wrens, together with the larger magpies and butcher birds. Here, too, are individual species of particular interest: the bower birds, which, in addition to their nests, build tunnel or tent-like structures of sticks and grass decorated with pieces of glass, shells and other colourful objects — and the lyrebird, which spreads its lacy tail like a fan to perform the most exquisite dances and can mimic innumerable bird calls and forest sounds.

But some of the most intriguing of Australia's unique birds are found outside the passerine group. The continent's largest bird, the flightless Emu, stands 1.5 metres tall, weighs up to 68 kilograms and can run at 50 kilometres an hour. Most Australians have never seen an Emu in the wild but they would have seen one or more of the parrots, for Australia is one of the world centres of these birds. About 50 species are endemic, and one important group, the screeching, crested cockatoos, is found only in this region.

There are birds of prey — the king of which is the soaring Wedge-tailed Eagle with a wing-span of 2.5 metres — and numerous waterbirds, including the world's only completely black swan. And here are found some of the world's most hard-working birds, the megapodes or incubator-birds, prodigious builders, found only in Australia and the northern islands, which, instead of sitting on their eggs, bury them in earthern incubators.

The lives and habits of these remarkable birds and mammals are described in more detail in the following chapters.

2 Along the Wild Ocean's Shores

The island continent of Australia is largely enclosed by two great oceans — the Indian and the Pacific — and its coastline extends for more than 20 000 kilometres. It is not surprising that this vast distance, crossing more than 30 degrees of latitude, encompasses almost every kind of coastal landform and habitat: rocky cliffs, sheltered lakes and sand dunes, wide bays and deep inlets, river estuaries and tidal flats. This short section deals primarily with the southern coasts, for it is here that some of the most interesting mammals and birds are to be found.

Across the mouth of the Great Australian Bight and through the narrow, storm-tossed waters of Bass Strait the 'Roaring Forties' lash the cold southern Indian Ocean eastwards. In these waters and on the small, rocky offshore islands, most groups of Australia's marine mammals are found. In addition to more than 20 species of whales ranging from less than six metres long to more than 30 metres long, the region supports colonies of seals and sealions, penguins and migratory sea birds.

The Australian Fur Seal was once common in very large herds and, as its name implies, was hunted commercially for its hide. Sealing was a thriving industry along the southern coast (as was whaling) even before settlement and thousands upon thousands of these harmless creatures were clubbed and knifed to death for their hides and oil. In the early 1800s hauls of up to 100 000 skins at a time were taken. The falling demand for seal products saved these docile animals and today they live peacefully on rocky islets dotted between Victoria and the Great Australian Bight. Colonies of as many as 5000 have been seen in the breeding season when the males or bulls gather as many as 50 females in a harem which they guard jealously against rival bulls.

The Australian Sealion or White-capped Hair Seal is the largest seal in Australian waters and may grow up to three and a half metres long. The Sealions are so named because they have a thick mane of fur which in the Australian Sealion is a yellowish colour, becoming almost white in old bulls. The diet of this large mammal comprises fish and small penguins which are captured as they leave their burrows on the rookeries. Like most seals it has the habit of swallowing pebbles, presumably as some kind of digestive aid; there may be a dozen or more granite stones in its stomach, ranging in size from about 25 millimetres in diameter to the size of a tennis ball, and together weighing anything from two kilograms upwards.

The Australian seals may at times be found sharing the habitat of the world's smallest penguin, the Little or Fairy Penguin, which nests and breeds along the southern and eastern coasts from Fremantle in Western Australia to Moreton Bay near Brisbane: at Phillip Island in Westernport Bay, Victoria, the birds have become an established tourist attraction. Little Penguins build a nest of grass or seaweed in holes or burrows scraped beneath grass tussocks, and live in well-established rookeries. The grey and white birds are about half a metre high; they swim fast, using their flippers, and feed on small fish such as pilchards. The adults may spend a day or so at sea catching fish which they bring back to the rookery in a semi-digested state to feed the young. Like all penguins, they are unable to fly.

By contrast, some of the great long-distance fliers of the bird world, the petrels, albatrosses and shearwaters, are found in Australian waters (though none of these birds is a permanent resident).

The appropriately named Wandering Albatross has no true 'home'. This great bird, with a wingspan of over three metres, breeds on Macquarie Island in the sub-Antarctic, and is believed to spend most of its life circumnavigating the southern seas in an easterly direction; it may spend as long as several years at a time at sea without making landfall. In winter the bird moves north; it regularly visits the coastal waters just south of Sydney and may be seen as far north as the Tropic of Capricorn, gliding and circling gracefully without appearing to move its wings.

Another marathon flier is the Tasmanian Mutton Bird or Short-tailed Shearwater. This bird nests on islands in Bass Strait, on Bruny Island and a few parts of the mainland coast around south-eastern Australia. In autumn, when breeding is over, the birds fly north across the Pacific Ocean to the Arctic Circle and Alaska where they moult and are for a time flightless. The return journey brings the birds back along the east coast of Australia in September to complete a giant figure-eight journey roughly equivalent to circumnavigating the globe.

The long annual migration of the Mutton Bird has been the subject of much speculation among scientists. As an achievement it is all the more remarkable now that scientists have shown that most birds which make the journey return to the same burrow they left six months earlier. Somehow they manage to navigate by the sun and stars, travelling in huge flocks which have been reliably assessed at up to 400 000 birds in one day. The early navigator Matthew Flinders saw a stream of 'from 50 to 80 yards in depth and of 300 yards or more in breadth' (about 55 metres by 275 metres) which took a full hour and a half to pass him.

Probably the most common and widespread birds of the coasts are the gulls. The grey-and-white Silver Gull, also known as the Seagull, may also be found in large numbers further inland around lakes, inlets and garbage dumps, for it is a scavenger with a wide-ranging diet and is attracted to settlements. The larger black-and-white Pacific Gull feeds primarily from the surface of the sea on fish and other marine creatures and is usually seen singly or in pairs.

The least common bird of the coasts is the Cape Barren Goose whose numbers are limited and whose lineage is puzzling. A goose-like bird, thought by some to be related to the shelducks and by others to the grey geese of the northern hemisphere, it was first sighted on Cape Barren Island, north of Tasmania, in 1798. The breeding range of this bird is so restricted that it was for a time threatened with extinction but concerted efforts by conservationists halted shooting by farmers and fishermen and the bird's numbers are now increasing.

The largest of Australia's eared seals is the huge Australian Sealion with its distinguishing yellowish mane of coarse hair. It is a non-migratory animal and is fond of eating penguins.

Seabirds: Travellers and Fishers

The fabled Albatross (left), while not restricted to Australia, is at home on the southern oceans; the largest species is the Wandering Albatross with a wing span of over three metres. It has a hooked, horny-plated bill with tubular nostrils and like many of the marine birds, it feeds its single young by regurgitation. Weighing up to nine kilograms, this bird has enormous endurance and rarely visits land except to breed. The Black Cormorant (below) is the largest cormorant and is found in marine or fresh water habitats. A proficient swimmer, it is able to pursue its prey underwater, though its plumage lacks the waterproof quality of other aquatic birds and can become so saturated that the bird is forced to land and dry out its feathers.

A Symbol of Wildlife Survival

Through the efforts of conservationists the Cape Barren Goose (above), once rare and threatened with extinction, now grazes in flocks or pairs on many southern islands. This extraordinary bird seems unrelated to any other genus. It is a strong flier — the goose-like body is magnificent when stretched out in flight — but feeds entirely on ground vegetation. It probably mates for life and lays as many as seven eggs. The bird has a honking or trumpeting call but may make a grunting noise when exhibiting sometimes aggressive territorial behaviour during breeding. More common are the scavenging Silver Gulls (right), often seen squabbling noisily over morsels of marine offal or scraps.

This handsomely striking bird is the
Australian Gannet. It prefers to hunt
in parties and will plummet from a
great height to capture fish which are
then swallowed whole underwater.
The birds are common to the southern
coasts.

3 Forests and Woodlands of the East

Australia is the flattest continent of the world. Only in the east, where the Great Dividing Range curves like the vertebrae of a submerged backbone from Cape York in the north to south-eastern Victoria, are there mountains worthy of the name. On these highlands most of Australia's rain falls, and where the rain falls the forests grow.

The dominant forest tree of the east — and, indeed, of the continent — is the *Eucalyptus* or 'gum tree'. This genus of myrtle contains more than 600 species and accounts for 95 per cent of the forests. One species, the Mountain Ash, grows to a height of more than 90 metres; it is not only the tallest hardwood tree, it is the largest flowering plant in the world.

The variety of the eucalypts is enormous. They range from the forest giants to the low, straggly mallees which thrive in arid regions and grow no more than nine metres high. On the high slopes of the ranges there are many areas of hardwood forests where the tall eucalypts dominate; at lower altitudes these give way to more open woodland with stands of lesser eucalypts and acacias.

Many of Australia's native animals and birds live in a close association with the eucalypts: they feed on the flowers, fruits, leaves or buds; they shelter among the branches or they make their nests in tree-holes. The marsupial Koala is totally adapted to the large gums. This bear-like creature, with its thick, woolly fur and dark, rubbery muzzle, spends almost its entire life in the trees and will feed only on the leaves of about a dozen species, notably the manna gum, the messmate, swamp and peppermint gums, the stringybark, red gum and several box gums. Although the manna gum is favoured, the new leaves of this tree at a certain time of the year contain a poisonous substance, cineol. Koalas can take three to five times as much of this substance as humans but they usually move to another species of eucalypt when it occurs.

The eucalypt forests are also the home for many species of possums, particularly the gliders. These possums, which range greatly in size and belong to several genera, have, in common, a fleshy flap or membrane extending along the sides of the body from the front legs to the hind legs. When the possum is climbing or at rest, these folds are bunched up, but when it makes a gliding leap from one high branch to another, the membrane opens out like a fixed wing or parachute. Most of these possums feed on insects and (though not exclusively) on the buds and blossoms of eucalypts.

The fruits and flowers of the eucalypts also form an important part of the diet of one of Australia's most brilliantly-coloured birds, the Crimson Rosella. This well-known parrot is found throughout eastern and south-eastern Australia in forest and open woodlands where it nests in hollow limbs or tree holes.

Similar nesting sites are favoured by the Laughing Kookaburra, a well-known bird of the hardwood forests. This bird, with its cackling call resembling raucous laughter, is, however, carnivorous. Kookaburras are a species of kingfisher which have adapted to the forest habitat; instead of hunting fish they prey on snakes and small reptiles which live on the forest floor. Studies have shown that kookaburras live in family groups consisting of the parent birds and one or more offspring, and that each group selects its own area of bushland which it regards as its territory and will defend against the intrusion of other kookaburras.

Not all the fauna in forested country lives in the trees; the undergrowth is the habitat of many unique marsupials. One of the largest is the stocky, coarse-haired wombat, which makes its home in burrows or fallen logs and emerges at night to forage for native grasses, the roots of shrubs and occasionally the bark of trees. Weighing up to 45 kilograms, it is quite unlike the other marsupials in appearance and despite its powerful build and large, sharp claws, is quite inoffensive.

A much more ferocious marsupial is the Tasmanian Devil, found only in rocky, wooded parts of Tasmania. A small, stocky animal with powerful jaws and large, strong teeth, it preys on small wallabies, rats, birds, possums, rabbits, snakes and lizards and on carrion. It takes its prey whole, crunching up the bones with its specially adapted teeth. Although the animals do not attack humans unless provoked, the males are very antagonistic towards their rivals.

In forest streams and rocky pools the shy Platypus slips from its burrow into the waters to search the mud for aquatic insects, tadpoles, worms and shrimps. This curious creature, possessing the features of so many apparently unrelated species, grows to a length of from 45 to 60 centimetres, including the tail, and the adult male weighs about two kilograms. The body is covered with fur and the skin is very loose, as if it does not fit properly. One of the most curious features is the muzzle or bill. Broad, flat and shaped like a duck's bill it is however, moist, soft and flexible, unlike the horny beak of a bird, and pitted with tiny sense pores which the animal uses under water to find its way about and locate its food.

As the forest thins out on the lower slopes and the tall trees give way to more open, grassed woodlands there is a corresponding change in the wildlife population. This is a major habitat of the largest of all marsupials, the kangaroos and wallabies. (The only distinction between kangaroos and wallabies is their size.)

The kangaroo is probably the most famous of all Australia's native fauna. It is unusual in many ways; instead of running on all fours it hops and its hind feet are powerful and especially developed to give the animal its graceful, bounding movement. The other well-known features of the kangaroos are the long powerful tail (sometimes as long as the rest of the body) and the pouch in which the young or 'joeys' develop and live until they are old enough to fend for themselves. Kangaroos and wallabies are herbivorous, feeding wholly upon grasses and similar vegetation, and their body structure is designed for grazing. The forelegs are very small because they are not needed for fighting enemies or catching or tearing prey as in some other animals. The large tail at times acts like a third leg or balance and is used to push the animal along when it is grazing.

At a moment's notice this Grey Kangaroo could go leaping away with a graceful, hopping motion capable of taking it up to forty kilometres an hour. The animal stands about as high as a man.

Creatures of the Night and Day

The predatory, nocturnal Barn Owl (left) watches unblinkingly before pouncing on mice, beetles and reptiles. The soft flesh of its prey is digested in the usual way, whilst the harder portions of nail, bone and fur are regurgitated as hard pellets. The beautifully coloured Crimson Rosella (below) is one of the best-known native parrots. Active during the day, it frequents heavily-timbered ranges, feeding mainly on grass seeds. By contrast, the Common Wombat (right) is seldom seen by day. Thick-set and tail-less, it can grow to about a metre long and weigh up to 45 kilograms. A solitary, inoffensive vegetarian creature, it forages at night and sleeps during the day in its burrow.

High in the Tall Forest Canopy

The carnivorous Wedge-tailed Eagle (left) has an impressive wing span of over 2.5 metres, making it the largest Australian raptore. It has the typical hooked beak of birds of prey and when hovering or soaring is distinguishable by the wedge-shaped tail and upward-turning wing tips. Another forest-dweller is the Squirrel Glider (below), similar to but slightly larger than the Sugar Glider (see page 37) and with a more pronounced dorsal stripe. The Common Brush-tailed Possum (right) has a diversified diet of many types of buds and leaves, also carrion. It is larger and slower than most other possums and is probably the most common marsupial in Australia.

An Animal that Puzzled Scientists

A mammal that lays eggs, the Platypus was once
considered to be some sort of taxidermist's joke,
with its flat tail, furry body, webbed feet and
duck-like bill. However, these aquatic adaptations have ensured the Platypus' survival; it is
probably the oldest furred animal in Australia,
if not the world. It nuzzles through the mud on
the bottom of streams with its sensitive,
rubbery bill locating and eating astonishingly
large amounts of yabbies and worms. Normally
it makes a tunnel with several entrances under
tree roots in a river bank, but during the breeding season, the female digs a long single-opening
tunnel above water level with a nest-chamber.
The young are suckled from milk-secreting pores
on the female's underbelly.

Koalas: At Home in the Treetops

The soft-furred Koala, with its rubbery nose and beady eyes, is a relative of the possums. Koalas evolved to a treetop habitat and their short limbs and strong, sharp claws are especially adapted to climbing. Being nocturnal, this appealing marsupial curls up sleepily in the fork of a gum tree during the day. Koalas have a backward-opening pouch for carrying the young, and mouth pockets for storing and carrying food. The animal's distribution is governed by the particular species of eucalypt on which it feeds and its digestive system is modified to cope with this limited diet. The offspring of the Koala go straight into the pouch after birth and even after leaving its warm confines will stay with the mother for a considerable time.

Kangaroos: The Largest Marsupials

The Grey Kangaroo (left, below), standing nearly two metres tall when fully grown, is the eastern representative of the kangaroos, the largest of all marsupials. Structured admirably for that graceful, hopping motion so typical of kangaroos, it has proportionally huge hind quarters with extended, flat feet and a long strong tail which swings up and down with every leap. The Grey is a gregarious animal, living and grazing in mobs of 10 to 30 animals. The Black-tailed or Swamp Wallaby (right) lives in a wide range of habitats but is most plentiful in swamp country with thick, impenetrable vegetation and steep-sided rock gullies. Nearly all kangaroos, including the wallabies, eat only grass and are shy animals.

The Kookaburra: Sharp-eyed Hunter

Kookaburras are a large species of kingfisher, although their plumage lacks the typical vividness and they have long since ceased to fish. Having keen eyesight they can sit among the treetops and spot small prey on the ground, but lacking the predator's normal assets of strong feet and hooked bill, they kill snakes and lizards by lashing them against a branch. Bandicoots (below) belong to a marsupial group distinguishable by long, pointed snouts. They have a rat-like appearance, with stubby limbs and long hind feet. The common Southern Short-nosed Bandicoot (pictured) has coarse, dark hair and feeds nocturnally on worms, insects and snails, for which it scrabbles about in leaf mould or loose soil.

Night Gliders among the Treetops

Glider possums possess flaps of skin between the fore and hind limbs which spread to act as vanes and enable the animals to move from treetop to treetop in great gliding leaps while the tail acts as a rudder. They are nocturnal, feeding on nectar, leaf tips and sometimes insects. The Feathertail Glider (left) is one of the most delicate and attractive, whilst the Greater Glider (right) is much larger, with big ears, furry tail and a long, thick, bushy coat. The wider-ranging Squirrel Glider (below left) is distinguishable by dark brown head stripes. Less common is the Tasmanian Devil (below) whose massive, strong teeth give it a ferocious appearance and suit its carnivorous diet of small mammals, birds and reptiles which it eats whole.

The handsome male Satin Bowerbird
constructs a complicated bower of
sticks to house his female-attracting
collection of blue and yellow objects
such as fruit, feathers and bits of glass.

4 Life in the Damp Rain Forests

The rainforests of Australia have always held a special fascination for naturalists. This is partly because they contain such an abundance of plant and animal life, and partly because, being relatively compact and well-defined areas, they offer ideal opportunities for studying the specialized adaptations animals make to their environment.

Classic rainforests, where the rainfall is between 1500 and 2500 millimetres a year (60 to 100 inches), form only about one per cent of Australia's vegetation and are limited to a number of areas dotted along the east coast from Cape York Peninsula to as far south as latitude 31°. There are, however, similar areas in other parts of the continent which are commonly called rainforest and where the local rainfall is between 1000 and 1500 millimetres a year. In this chapter the term 'rainforest' is used in its broadest sense and as a distinction from the 'dry' eucalypt-dominated forest described in the previous chapter.

The vegetation in a typical rainforest comprises two or more distinct 'layers'. The top layer is formed by tall trees such as eucalypts and kauris which may grow close together and block out much of the sunlight, making the area directly beneath dark and damp, and providing an ideal habitat for mosses, lichens and ferns. In more open rainforest there is a middle layer of medium-height trees such as native figs and palms and, where the sunlight penetrates, a bottom layer of thick undergrowth.

In these damp, humid environments, especially in the north, all forms of life flourish. In some areas of the Queensland rainforest, for instance, something like 300 species of trees, more than 50 mammals and more than 300 species of birds, together with an even greater wealth of insect life, have been recorded in areas whose boundaries do not exceed one hundred or so kilometres.

As in all forests, the fauna is a mixture of tree-dwelling and ground-dwelling creatures. All of them show evidence of the ways in which they have adapted to the environment, many in remarkable ways. Some of the most interesting rainforest birds, for instance, have abandoned their traditional reliance on flight and spend the greater part of their lives close to the forest floor.

An outstanding example is the Cassowary, second only to the Emu among native birds in size and, like the Emu, a bird that has lost the ability to fly; five species are found in northern Australia and in New Guinea. Although the Cassowary stands from a metre to one-and-a-half metres high, it is often difficult to see because it lives in very dense scrub. One of its most obvious features is the horny casque or helmet crowning its head and serving to protect the bird's head and eyes as it pushes its way through the tangled undergrowth. The Cassowary lives on fallen flowers, fruit seeds and insects on the forest floor, and its large, powerful, three-toed feet are well suited for scratching in the debris. Its feathers are dark, shiny and tough, but the bird's neck, which is naked, is a bright blue and flanked with prominent red, fleshy wattles.

An even more striking bird of the forest floor is the Superb Lyrebird. During the reproductive season the male lyrebird builds mounds of forest debris which serve as platforms from which he makes complicated ceremonial displays. During these displays he opens and flaunts the delicate fan-like tail in a manner similar to that of a peacock. Although not brilliantly coloured like a peacock's tail, it makes a dazzling sight, flashing white and fragile in the gloom of the forest. At the same time the bird emits a multitude of quite loud calls. Some of these mimic the calls of other birds, while others reproduce sounds the bird apparently has heard in the forest, such as saw-mill whistles.

In the same way as some species usually associated with an aerial habitat have, in the rainforests, adapted to life on the ground, so some terrestrial creatures have taken to the trees. Here, for instance, we find tree frogs, tree snakes and tree ants — there are even tree kangaroos, described in a later chapter.

The marsupials of the rainforest include both tree-dwellers, such as possums, and ground-dwellers, such as scrub wallabies. The common Ring-tail and its close relatives are among the most widely found possums. Like many possums, the tail of this species, which is two-thirds as long as its body, is prehensile, that is, capable of grasping. Its grip is enhanced by a naked area of skin which extends from the tip to about half-way along on the under side. The tail is used frequently when the possum is climbing and the animal may hang suspended solely by its tail in order to reach buds or fruit. When the possum is resting or inactive the tail is coiled up in a ring. Several species of ring-tail are found in the rainforest and north-eastern regions of Australia. The Striped Ring-tail, however, is exclusively a rainforest-dweller and differs in one significant way from all its relatives. This possum has evolved fur with a greenish hue which, together with its dark stripes, give it perfect camouflage among the dark moss- and lichen-covered limbs of the forest.

The Sugar Glider, which is found in, but is not restricted to, the rainforests, is one of the most beautiful of all marsupials. Its fur is ash-grey, with a prominent dark stripe, and its squirrel-like body is only eighteen centimetres long with a tapering, slightly longer tail. Although its diet consists mainly of insects, buds, blossoms and fruit, it has a particular liking for the sweet nectar obtained from the blossoms and will eat honey, sugar or jam if they are available. It is one of the most efficient of the gliders and its downwards leaps are known to have exceeded 45 metres.

The ability to span such distances can be a useful defence, for even in the peace of the rainforest there are predators, like the ferocious Tiger Cat, ready to strike. A primitive, marsupial version of the feline cat, this strikingly spotted animal catches birds and small mammals. Its reflexes are very fast and it is an active climber, aided by sharp claws and foot pads which grip efficiently. The Tiger Cat grows to about 1.3 metres long and hunts at night, sheltering during the day in hollow logs or rocky hideaways. It belongs to the Dasyuridae family which includes the Tasmanian Devil and the extinct Tasmanian Wolf (Thylacine).

The stocky, flightless Cassowary of the northern jungles has a horny, shield-like 'helmet' on its head and a colourful, featherless neck. Australia's second largest bird is a wary, timid creature which can run and swim strongly.

Two Birds with Clever Disguises

The Tawny Frogmouth (above) is a nocturnal hunter and spends the day perched stiffly on a tree limb, resembling with incredible accuracy a broken-off branch. Mistakenly called a Mopoke (it is not an owl), it feeds on insects and mice. A more timid mimic, the Lyrebird frequents dense mountain forests and can reproduce sounds made by other bush creatures and by man with amazing fidelity. With its long tail neatly folded (top right) it appears an elegant but unremarkable bird. However, when the male performs his stately courtship dance on a cleared mound (left), the splendid tail plumage lifts and spreads, covering the head and body with delicate brown and white fronds.

The Potoroo: A Nest-builder

The Potoroo or Long-nosed Rat-kangaroo is one of the smallest members of the kangaroo family. Like other rat-kangaroos it builds a grass nest beneath forest debris; it can also use its tail to hold and carry nesting material. Although now rare on the Australian mainland, the Potoroo is common in Tasmania where it favours swampy country with dense undergrowth, rain forest and wet sclerophyll forest. It has the typically long hind feet and body pouch of the large kangaroos but has a bandicoot-like appearance and a strange galloping gait using all four feet. The Potoroo is a strictly nocturnal feeder, utilising its fore feet for eating and preying on insects and its snout and claws for digging up roots and tubers.

Bizarre Faces in the Dark Forest

The bats, weird creatures of the night, have always been associated with fear and superstition. But the heavily wrinkled lips and sharp teeth of the White Mastif Bat (left), together with its strange bone-and-membrane wings and rat-like tail, belie its gentle nature. Recognizable by a narrow white stripe on both sides of the body, this bat can scurry about on the ground like a rodent and is a specialized feeder on fruit and blossom. Boyd's Forest Dragon (below) leers open-mouthed when faced by an enemy. This lizard lives in the rain forest of northern Queensland where its grey-green to lime-green colouration blends with the surrounding lush jungle. By squatting motionless on lichen-covered branches it is imperceptible in the forest growth.

The Ringtail: An Agile Climber

The tail of the Common Ringtail possum (above) is long, tapered and strong; it can be curled up tightly in a ring or used for grasping branches, making tree-climbing very efficient. Smaller than a domestic cat, the Ringtail feeds at night on leaves and fruit and has a habit of 'freezing' when danger approaches. The untidy nests or dreys of the possums are often found in coastal scrub or forests where the trees grow thickly. The wide-ranging Sugar Glider (right) is not strictly a rain forest dweller, but inhabits the forest fringes where it glides from tree to tree. Smaller than the Squirrel Glider but otherwise not easily distinguishable, the Sugar Glider is partly carnivorous and will even eat small birds.

Three that Hide among the Trees

The trees and undergrowth of the northern rain forests are the natural habitat of a myriad of creatures. Among the tree-dwellers is the Two-colour or Dwarf Tree Frog (right) with legs elongated for jumping and outspread digits concealing adhesive discs which enable the little green and pink frog to cling to a variety of surfaces. The Green Python (left) is another creature of the warm rain forest. Its colouration provides excellent camouflage as it slithers silently through the branches. The tree-dwelling ants (below) belong to the group of weaver ants and are remarkable for their nest-building: here, some workers are pulling the leaf edges together while others bring larvae to produce silken threads with which to 'sew' the leaves together.

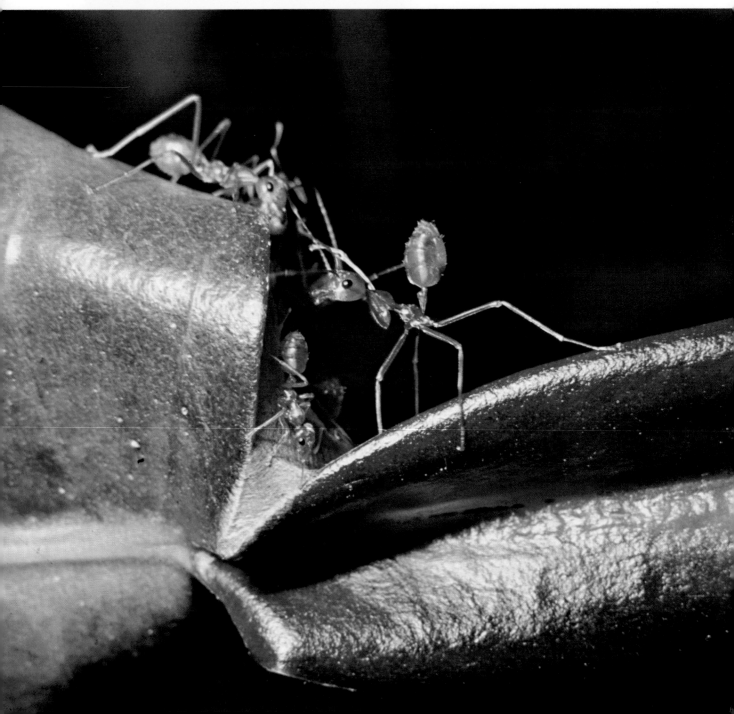

A primitive version of the feline cat, the spotted, marsupial Tiger Cat is a shy yet ferocious carnivore whose hard nails and serrated foot pads make it a proficient tree-climber.

5 The Scrubs and Dry Grasslands

A very large proportion of Australia's land surface is covered, in varying degrees, by scrubs and dry grasslands. Depending on the presence of water and the regularity of rainfall, the vegetation in these regions ranges from areas lightly timbered with well-spaced clumps of hardy trees, to drought-resistant scrub such as 'mallee' and plains covered sparsely with native grasses and varieties of salt bush. These extensive, flat areas tend to be hot during the day and, because of the lack of cloud cover, cold at night. In most inland areas the conventional differences between the seasons are less well-defined; generally there are only two seasons, the 'dry' and the 'wet'.

The main sustenance for life in these regions comes from the native vegetation which, due to the low rainfall, is too sparse to support great numbers of large animals. Rather, the fauna includes a high proportion of insect-eaters, seed-eaters and other vegetarians, whose diet comprises the native grasses and the leaves, fruits and blossoms of trees and shrubs. The exceptions are in areas where the native birds and animals have survived — even flourished — by feeding on cultivated crops, especially grain. Meat-eaters, such as the dingo and the birds of prey which feed off the small herbivores, are, of course, represented but their populations are relatively small and limited by the restricted supply of food.

The Red Kangaroo of the inland gained its name because the males are usually a striking reddish colour. The females are a smoky-blue but there are many variations in the colours of both sexes in different localities. The Red Kangaroo is the largest of all marsupials, often growing to a height of more than 1.8 metres (abour six feet) when standing. It lives in groups which can number one hundred or more and the male, when bounding at full speed, may reach a speed of almost 50 kilometres (about 30 miles) an hour. The leaping power of kangaroos is recorded in many tales of the Australian bush and some of these stories are not as far-fetched as they may sound at first. The large kangaroos can certainly jump 7.6 metres (about 25 feet) in a single bound and there are records of leaps as long as 12 metres. Some kangaroos can also leap considerable heights. Many are able to leap an obstacle 2.4 metres high (about eight feet) and a jump of more than three metres (about ten feet) has been recorded.

Medium-sized marsupials are not plentiful in these regions: the most interesting species include the Hairy-nosed Wombat, a scrub-dwelling relative of the Common Wombat; the Numbat, a beautifully-furred termite-eater found mainly in forest fringes in Western Australia, and the Marsupial Mole, a rare and curious creature with no eyes or external ears, which has been found in mulga and salt bush on the fringes of the desert.

However, the scrubs and grasslands carry much larger populations of the smaller marsupials. These include the rat-kangaroos, small, rodent-like members of the kangaroo family; hare-wallabies; marsupial mice and marsupial rats. Many of these live in the undergrowth or among the grass tussocks, in holes, burrows or nests which they make from grass, and feed on insects or small non-marsupial rodents of which there are large numbers.

These small mammals, together with the introduced rabbits and small reptiles, form a major part of the diet of the birds of prey — eagles, hawks, falcons and their relatives — found in the scrubs and grasslands. Characteristics of these birds are a large wingspan and extremely keen vision. Their large wings enable them to glide, soar and sometimes hover high in the sky, riding the currents of warm air rising from the surface while their sharp eyes watch for any sign of prey. They have powerful, long-taloned feet for grasping and carrying away their victims and sharp, hooked beaks for tearing at their flesh.

Probably the best-known birds of the scrubs and grasslands, however, are the parrots, notably the various species of cockatoos and the budgerigars. The cockatoos are the largest members of the family and are characterized by their powerful, prominent beaks. Cockatoos live in and around the large eucalypts and their beaks are designed for stripping bark from the trees in order to find grubs on which they feed, and for breaking open the hard fruits of the eucalypts to reach the soft insides which they also eat. (They also eat the seeds of grasses and the seeds, fruits and berries of other plants and cultivated crops.) Their prominent, erectile crests are used for communication among the large groups in which they live. The budgerigar, a member of the family Psittacidae or 'true parrots' and one of the most popular cage birds in the world, is found in great numbers in the interior. A small, brilliantly coloured bird, it feeds exclusively on the seeds of grasses and herbaceous plants.

In parts of south-eastern Australia the ground is covered by a low, drought-resistant species of eucalyptus scrub called 'mallee'. This is the original habitat of one of Australia's most remarkable birds, the Mallee Fowl.

While most birds incubate their eggs by sitting on them, the Mallee Fowl places its eggs inside a large mound of rotting vegetation which, through the heat generated by natural decomposition, keeps the eggs warm. During the autumn the male bird digs a hole about one metre deep. In the ensuing months he fills this hole with leaves and twigs until he has built a mound about 0.3 metres (one foot) high, the contents of which gradually become wet from winter rains. In the top of this mound he makes another hole, which he fills with sand; this is the egg chamber. The entire construction is then covered with sandy soil and smoothed down. Thus covered, the wet vegetation begins to rot and give off heat.

The bird tests the temperature of the nest chamber by thrusting his beak into the sand. When the temperature is right, the female begins laying. Over a period of five months she may lay from 14 to 22 eggs which hatch progressively until it is time for the male to start building a new mound.

If the nesting chamber becomes too hot, the male removes some of the warm sand and replaces it with cool sand from around the mound. If it becomes too cool, as it may in autumn, the male reduces the amount of sand covering the eggs, to allow them to be warmed by the sun.

Regarded as pests by farmers, the noisy Galahs are spectacular in wheeling flock flight, flashing alternately rose-pink fronts and silver-grey backs. They are popular cage birds.

Two Parrots of the Grasslands

The Sulphur-crested or White Cockatoo (left) with its bright yellow crest, quizzical eyes, and ability to learn the art of 'talking', is a favourite amongst Australians. Larger than many other native parrots, it has the typical curved beak with the top mandible fitting over the lower, and can use its claws effectively as 'hands' to eat grass seeds and grain. It feeds in large flocks with a sentinel bird posted in a nearby tree; the crest is raised if the bird is alarmed. Next to the Galah, the Corella (below) is probably the most lively of Australian parrots; inland trees appear laden with white blossoms when a chattering flock of Corellas lands in them. These parrots are also well-known as cage-birds and, like other cockatoos, have an erectile crest of head-feathers.

A Spiny Survivor from the Past

The spiky coat of the Echidna or Spiny Anteater
provides a marvellous protection against enemies
and, like its relative the Platypus, this monotreme
has survived in its original form longer than most
other animals. It may be seen in stony areas
waddling along at dusk or in the early morning,
locating ants' nests by turning over stones with
its long, thin snout. Once ants are discovered,
the Echidna uses its well-adapted long, sticky
tongue to scoop them up in large numbers; if
disturbed it will roll up in a tight ball or dig
vertically into the ground. The elongated second
claw on the hind leg (right) is used for cleaning
among the spines. The female lays one egg,
which is carried in a pouch until it hatches.

Emu: The Largest Native Bird

The Emu is Australia's 'national bird', standing with a kangaroo on the official coat-of-arms. The continent's largest bird is incapable of flight and the highly modified feathers bounce bustle-like if this inquisitive, long-necked nomad is running. Being large, Emus have few natural enemies but if they become alarmed they will dash away frantically in a straight line, their long legs taking them at speeds of up to 50 kilometres an hour when hard pressed. The male bird incubates the five to 20 eggs and the young follow him about for a year after hatching. Although these birds eat almost anything — fruit, grass, seeds, insects — they live mainly in remote, dry, inland areas and will migrate in large numbers to available food.

The Mound-building Mallee Fowl

A well-known mound-builder is the subtly coloured Mallee Fowl (left and right) which lives in sparsely vegetated environments. The pyramid-shaped mound is scientifically constructed by the male so that rotting leaf mould within the pile of sand will create the required temperature to hatch the average of 20 eggs laid by the female. He then takes over incubation duties and controls the mound temperature by removing or adding material. Budgerigars (above) occur inland in huge flocks of up to 10 000 birds and are prized as cage birds throughout the world. They are very dependent on water, nomadic, and move south in late winter, nesting in great chattering flocks.

A Large Kangaroo of the Plains

The most common and widely spread species of
kangaroo in Australia is the Red Kangaroo
which lives in open plains and scrub. It is thinner
than the Grey, with longer limbs and a shorter,
more variably-coloured coat; females in eastern
regions are nick-named 'blue flyers' because of
their smoky-blue colour. Like the Greys they
are sociable animals, sometimes occurring in
mobs of hundreds. In all kangaroos, the young
is born as a furless, blind embryo and creeps
instinctively through its mother's fur to attach
itself to a nipple within the pouch where it
develops. The older male Reds can be aggressive
among themselves and will use their tail to prop
themselves up and 'box' with their fore feet.

Some Contrasts among Marsupials

Thick granulated foot pads help the Yellow-footed Rock Wallaby (below) to leap with amazing two-footed precision from rock to rock in accessible terrain. Being herbivorous, these wallabies depend entirely on the pockets of grass and other herbage found in rocky areas. Another much smaller marsupial, the solitary Numbat (right), feeds exclusively on ants and termites and has a narrow snout and long, thin tongue adapted for this purpose. In daylight it hunts for its prey among fallen trees and bush debris on the forest floors of southern Western Australia. The Spinifex or Plumed Pigeon (left) is essentially a ground bird, feeding on grass seeds and herb-like plants in open stony country with light scrub and clumps of spinifex.

Two Hunters of the Open Country

The Nankeen Kestrel (below) is often seen in Australia hovering over paddocks in lightly-timbered lowland country. It has a habit of dropping suddenly out of the sky to capture insects, mice and small reptiles. Because of these diet preferences, this well-known member of the falcon family is a valuable controller of pests in cultivated areas. Also called the Windhover or Sparrowhawk, it appears singly or in pairs and has a peculiar chattering call. The Spotted Harrier (left) is found mainly in open inland country and is a large member of the hawk family. A carnivorous bird, it is distinguishable by the owlish nature of its head and although mainly seen flying slowly over plains, it will feed while on the ground or on the wing.

A Remarkable Builder and Mimic

The large bower of the Spotted Bowerbird (below) is constructed of sticks, often beneath the low branches of a tree or bush near an orchard, the main source of food. White objects predominate in the collection this male gathers and displays to induce the female to the mating site. The male seems to use the same bower throughout the year and any nearby listener may be treated to amazing feats of mimicry in which the bird may reproduce many different sounds. The White-winged or Blue-and-white Wren (left) is a pretty little bird found in drier inland areas. Like most wrens, the males and females show different colour characteristics; the male is smartly decked out in a bi-colour combination while the female is a dowdy brown.

The Tunnelling Hairy-nosed Wombat

The numbers of the vulnerable Hairy-nosed Wombat (above) are diminishing because of its preference for treeless plains and because it is extremely selective in the herbage it eats. The heavily-built Wombat partly counteracts these disadvantages by laboriously digging a network of underground tunnels with several entrances and by having the ability to exist for long periods without water. It sleeps underground in the heat of day emerging only at night to forage for food. The tiny Black-throated or Parson Finch (right) feeds on seeds and insects in open grassland near watercourses. It builds an intriguing bottle-shaped nest of dried grass lined with feathers.

A menace to sheep-station owners, the
tawny-yellow Dingo is a wolf-like
relative of the domestic dog, with a
howl instead of a bark and ears that
remain erect. It is a savage killer and
a cunning hunter.

6 Along the Northern Waterways

The sub-equatorial coast of the far north of Australia is one of the continent's most
distinctive wildlife habitats. Here, in contrast to the southern portion of the continent,
the climate is characterized by heavy summer rains. During the months of November to
April the rainfall amounts to between 75 and 125 centimetres (30 to 50 inches) and the
temperature ranges between 25° and 30° C. 'Winter' (May to October) is the dry season,
when the rainfall does not exceed 12.5 centimetres (five inches).

These summer rains feed rivers and streams right across the northern coast and a glance
at a large-scale map of Australia will show at least 90 major rivers entering the sea between
Cape York and Broome. Surrounding their estuaries and deltas are extensive mudflats and
mangrove swamps, especially on the southern shores of the Gulf of Carpentaria. Further
inland, hundreds upon hundreds of square kilometres are covered by shallow swamps and
waterways which often merge into large areas of tropical grasslands.

These vast areas of shallow waters are extremely rich in both plant and animal life. The
range of vegetation includes eucalypts, mangroves and shrubby trees, tall reed-like grasses
and, on the waterways, extensive carpets of aquatic plants such as lotuses and native water-
lilies.

The fauna is very different from the dry-adapted creatures of the interior grasslands. Here
it is not the small furred marsupials which attract our attention, but rather those animals
whose lives are linked with the presence of water: crustaceans, frogs, fish, native water rats,
tortoises and crocodiles — and above all, the birds; for the northern shores and waterways
resemble more than anything a giant bird sanctuary.

The most striking group are the water birds which include some of Australia's largest
flying birds. The northern waterways support very large populations, since the marshes and
swamps are an almost constant source of food: small water animals, bulbs of aquatic plants,
insects, molluscs, frogs, tadpoles and fish. In addition, the tall reeds and other water grasses
offer efficient cover from predators and plenty of material for the constructing of nests.
These factors combine to produce ideal habitats for large numbers of permanent residents
as well as for many transient ones. The endemic birds include herons, egrets, rails, bitterns,

crakes, moorhens, swamphens, cormorants, grebes, ducks and many others.

Yet many of the groups which are significant in the northern hemisphere are barely represented in Australia. Australia has only one native crane, one stork and one swan. Ducks and geese amount to only eighteen species out of a world total of 148. (Great Britain, one twenty-fifth the size of Australia, has about 47 species.) The paucity of species in Australia is probably the result of the limited availability of water over much of the continent. In the waterways of the north, however, some of the native species are found in extremely large numbers.

Two examples are the Pied or Magpie Goose and the Whistle Duck. The latter is possibly the most beautiful of the native ducks. It is found in grass and forest areas throughout the north of the continent in both coastal and inland regions and can be quite common on the coasts of Queensland and northern New South Wales during inland droughts. Frequently the birds are seen in flocks which may number hundreds, camping in grass or perching in trees not far from water. The birds have relatively long legs which enable them to move rapidly as they forage for grass and other herbage. The common name refers to the bird's whistle-like call.

The Whistle Duck's habitat is often shared by another plentiful bird of the northern waterways, the Magpie Goose. This bird, possibly named for its magpie-like colouring, congregates in huge flocks around swamps, lagoons, mangrove flats, lakes and rivers and has proved a serious pest to commercial rice crops in the Northern Territory. Its natural food comprises aquatic animals and plants for which it searches in shallow waters.

Australia's only stork is the Jabiru or Black-necked Stork which is also found in Asia. One of the finest of the large flying birds it has the typical stork characteristics: a long bill and long legs which, in the adult, are bright red. Its nest, which is very large and shallow, is made of twigs in a tree growing near a swamp; one of these nests has been recorded as measuring 1.8 metres (six feet) across but only 152 millimetres (six inches) deep. It was placed in a tree 5.5 metres (eighteen feet) above the ground. The Jabiru is generally found singly or in pairs, probing the swamp waters with its long bill or jabbing at frogs and fish.

The Brolga, or Native Companion, is Australia's endemic crane and, although found in many parts of the continent, is plentiful in the northern grasslands. This stately bird congregates in large groups and is best-known for its performances of complicated ceremonies which have been called 'dances' and 'corroborees'. These dances are a typical behaviour of the cranes and are movement patterns which serve stimulatory functions leading to pair-formation and so to eventual mating. In the legends of the Australian Aboriginals, Brolga was a young girl who loved to dance but was captured by cannibals and ultimately turned into a bird, condemned to dance eternally.

Not all the birds associated with the waterways are waders or swimmers. The Azure Kingfisher is a cousin of the Laughing Kookaburra and a member of the group known as water kingfishers. Although not restricted to the north, it may be found along the northern waterways perching near the surface of the water where it hunts frogs, small fish, crayfish and other water animals which it grasps with its sharp, very long pointed beak. Its nest is made in the bank of a stream, where it digs a tunnel, usually about 15 centimetres long, at the end of which is a nesting chamber. The bird has extremely keen eyesight and a streamlined shape which allows it to dive easily into the water in pursuit of its prey.

The animals and birds of the north are, unfortunately, too abundant and varied to be adequately described here. Some further interesting examples of the tropical fauna are described in the following chapter.

The Jabiru, Australia's only true stork, is found near northern watercourses stalking about and occasionally jabbing at fish, frogs and crabs with its huge, elongated black bill.

Some Birds of the Northern Waters

Probably the most elegant and unusual of our native ducks is the Whistle Duck (right), formerly known as the Whistling Tree Duck. At dusk it grazes goose-like in flocks, eating only herbage, its long legs facilitating rapid movement over land. Although it stands like a goose, its flight is slow and feeble and its call is a thin whistle. Whistle Ducks may often be found in company with Magpie Geese (see pp.62-63). The latter feeds on aquatic animals as well as plants and emits a musical gabbling and honking. Once plentiful in the south, it now wades long-legged through the remaining swamps in the north and its only partially webbed feet enable it to perch ungoose-like in trees. The brilliantly coloured Azure Kingfisher (left) hunts alone or with a mate in typical kingfisher fashion. First it perches in a tree close to water, frequently bobbing its head, then dives into the water to capture a small fish, yabbie, frog or water-beetle. It has a wide distribution ranging from the north through the east to Tasmania. The Estuarine or Salt Water Crocodile of the northern shores (below) is one of the few dangerous Australian animals, but although it will attack and kill a man in certain circumstances, its main diet is fish and crayfish. The reptile grows to almost five metres long and its powerful jaws equip it admirably for a predatory life.

65

The Brolga: A Graceful Dancing Bird

Australia's only endemic crane, the Brolga, is sometimes known as the Native Companion. It is a tall, willowy bird standing about 1.2 metres high. It has a husky, bugling call and is graceful in flight. Centuries ago the Aboriginals were fascinated by the elegant, stately dances which seemed to be performed within groups of Brolgas as an expression of excitement. A pair or several birds will line up opposite each other, advancing and retiring amid much wing shaking and the occasional wild trumpeting. This delicately coloured bird feeds on insects, small reptiles and rodents and sometimes vegetable matter, and while some are nomadic others may remain in the same locality. Brolgas are found mainly on the inland grass plains.

The Australian Pelican may weigh
more than seven kilograms but
although a powerful flier and good
swimmer, its progress on land is slow
and clumsy. The characteristic pouch
beneath its bill can hold more than
thirteen litres.

7 Abundant Life in the Tropics

Approximately forty per cent of Australia's land area lies north of the Tropic of Capricorn
and more than half the State of Queensland and eighty per cent of the Northern Territory
are within the tropics. Although about half of this area is semi-arid country, the rainforests,
woodlands and grasslands of the far north and north-east are typical of tropical vegetation.

Here the rainfall is substantial and the temperatures high and remarkably constant (the
extreme range is only about 15°). In north-east Queensland, where the Great Dividing Range
reaches its widest point, there are extensive highlands.

The wildlife of the tropics is notable, above all, for an abundance of species and for the
large populations of certain species. There are, for instance, more species of butterflies in
tropical Queensland than in the whole of the rest of Australia, while the number of seabirds
found on a single coral island may run into tens of thousands. Here, too, are found many of
the 'giants' of Australia's fauna and flora: the Queensland Groper, a formidable fish of bays
and estuaries which can grow to 1.8 metres (six feet) long and weigh up to 363 kilograms
(800 lbs); the world's largest reptile, the Estuarine Crocodile which grows to 6.7 metres
(22 feet) long; the largest possum and the largest mollusc. This chapter will deal with two of
the most important tropical habitats: the wet forests and the coral reefs.

The tropical forests are dark and gloomy at ground level beneath the almost impenetrable
canopy formed by the crowns of tall trees. There is no wind and the heavy rains reach the
ground only by trickling down the tree trunks and dripping from the thick, shiny, green
leaves (eighty per cent of the leaves in these forests have 'drip tips' to direct the water
downwards). The humidity hovers around ninety per cent night and day and the temperature
varies only slightly throughout the year. Shut off from sunlight, plant grows on plant in
order to survive; vines and other twining plants cling to the tree trunks, while parasites like
orchids and fungi draw nourishment directly from their hosts. Where a little light penetrates
there are many palms and more than 200 species of ferns, some among the largest in the
world with fronds 4.5 metres (fifteen feet) long.

Two of Australia's most interesting marsupials are found only in the tropical forests.
Lumholtz's Tree Kangaroo is, as its name suggests, a kangaroo that lives in the trees. It is

found on the Atherton Tablelands, in a region of frequent and heavy rainfall. It is a stockily-built animal with a rounded head unlike that of a typical kangaroo and a tail measuring about 66 centimetres (26 inches) — roughly the same length as its body. This large marsupial weighs about 10.4 kilograms (23 pounds) and feeds on vines, fruit and other herbage. The Tree Kangaroo is not as graceful and agile as the possums but is a powerful leaper and crashes through the branches as if unafraid of falling. Its remarkable tail, which does not taper like the tail of most other kangaroos and is not capable of grasping branches as a possum's can, probably serves to secure the animal's balance.

The other marsupial of interest is the Cuscus, the largest and strongest of all the possums. The head and body of this animal measure about 66 centimetres (26 inches) long and its tail, which measures somewhat less, is naked along the final half. The round head, hidden ears and bare, yellowish face of the Cuscus give it a very monkey-like appearance, and its habit of hanging upside down supported by the firm grip of its bare-tipped tail has more than once caused it to be mistaken for a monkey. In its movements, however, the Cuscus has none of the agility of the monkey. It seems to move determinedly, almost sluggishly, as it feeds in the trees on leaves and fruit, although it can apparently move quickly enough to catch small marsupials and birds and if it is threatened by a predator such as a forest python it will snarl and yap at its attacker, lashing out with its powerful, sharp claws. It is active at night and curls up in a tree during the day, its presence betrayed only by the strong musky odour it exudes.

By far the most outstanding natural feature of the tropical north is the Great Barrier Reef, a vast chain of coral reefs and islands which extends for 2000 kilometres from just north of Brisbane to the island of New Guinea.

The Great Barrier Reef is the product of the tiny coral animal and has often been called the largest construction made by living creatures, though it is important to remember that the 'reef' is not a single structure but rather a collection of natural formations. The coral animal or polyp is a relative of the sea anemone but differs from it in two important ways. Firstly, the adult animal has no means of propulsion; secondly, it has the ability to extract calcium from the sea water. The body of the animal is divided into a number of sections by flat vertical tissues and the calcium absorbed from the water is deposited along these sections and on the base of the animal so that it eventually becomes enclosed in a stony cup of its own making. When the living creature dies the cups remain embedded in the calcareous lump the coral animals have formed. Most coral polyps are only about the size of a pin's head and the rate at which they deposit calcium is very slow. Studies made on the Great Barrier Reef indicate that some of the corals there have grown at the rate of 49 metres (160 feet) in 1,000 years. Over the centuries the corals have built up the reefs which now spread over 207,000 square kilometres.

In the warm tropical waters many molluscs grow to considerable size. The Bailer Shell, from which ornamental lampshades were made and once used by the native tribes of the north to bail their canoes, grows to 46 centimetres (eighteen inches) long and contains a living animal which may weigh more than a kilogram. The Giant Clam, the largest of the molluscs, can weigh more than 226 kilograms (500 pounds) but despite its formidable appearance is not, as legend suggests, in the habit of snapping closed on the legs of unwary divers. Not all the molluscs of the reefs, however, are harmless. Many are flesh-eaters, preying on other living molluscs and sea creatures. Some are poisonous, like the Cone Shells, which first sting their victims then rasp away their flesh with their abrasive ribbon-tongue. Stings from the Venomous Cone Shell are known to have caused the deaths of at least five people.

The brush-like tip on the tongue of the swift-flying, colourful Rainbow Lorikeet is specially adapted for extracting nectar from seasonal flowers such as eucalyptus blossoms.

Wildlife of the Great Barrier Reef

In the tropic waters of the Great Barrier Reef marine creatures flourish. The Bailer Shell (left) measures about 45 centimetres and is prized for its smooth shape and creamy-orange colour. This melon-shaped shell was used by natives for scooping water out of their canoes. The Bailer Shell lives and feeds in the sandy mud of the Barrier Reef region and across northern Australia. A much larger occupant of these waters is the Giant Clam (below). This biggest of all bivalve molluscs is enclosed by two scalloped shells more than a metre long, and although it gains most of its food by simply extracting minute organisms from the water, it also 'farms' its own plant organisms within the thick mantle margin of the shell.

Sooty Terns by the Ten Thousands

Flocks of up to 50 000 Sooty Terns (over page)
can be seen on or about the northern island
areas. These small, smartly-plumaged marine
birds are also called Wideawake Terns because
of their querulous cry of 'Wideawake, Wideawake!'. The Loggerhead variety of sea turtle
(above) is characterized by a long neck and
although not as common as the Green Turtle, it
occurs in large numbers in the Great Barrier Reef
waters. Like all sea turtles, it lays a clutch of
eggs in a hole well up the beach, covers them
with sand and leaves the young to fend for
themselves. The large, greenish Mud Crab (right)
is found in northern mangrove regions and is
well-known for its size and edibility.

The Harmless Freshwater Crocodile

Smaller than the Estuarine Crocodile (page 65), the Freshwater or Johnston's Crocodile (left) is a fierce-looking but timid creature which grows up to three metres long. These reptiles have been slaughtered in hundreds for their valuable skins and are now plentiful only in the swamps or rivers of remote northern inland areas. They live on small mammals, reptiles and fish, occasionally taking water birds, and are quite harmless to man if left unmolested. The Red-browed Fig Parrot (below) is a small, stocky parrot with a short tail and a patch of red feathers above the nostrils. The birds are found in north-eastern Australia, where they live and feed in the trees on fruit, especially native figs, and seeds.

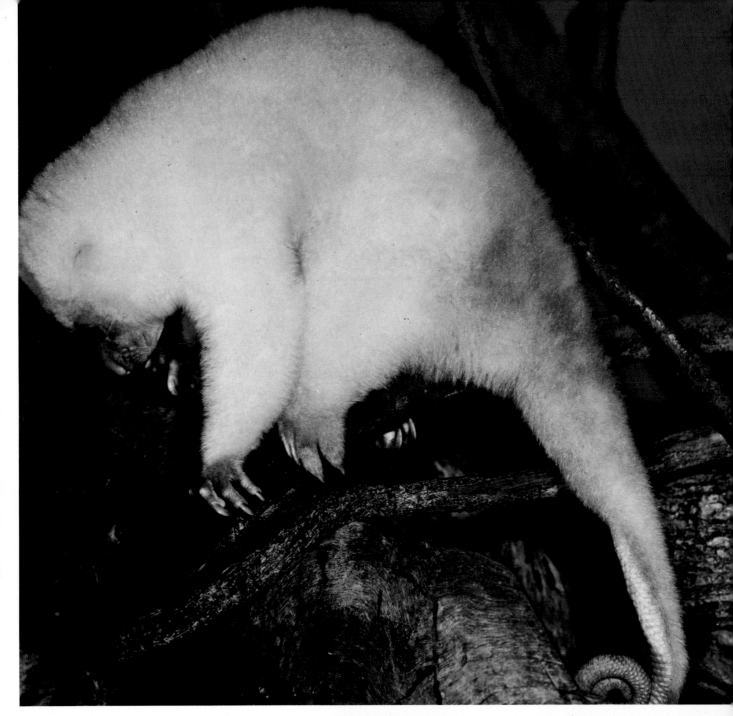

Two Climbers with Long Tails

The largest of the Australian possums, the
Cuscus (above) has a long, partially hairless
tail, small round ears and powerful claws. There
are two species, with basically grey or spotted
fur, although paler and even albino versions
(pictured) are not rare. The Cuscus moves
slowly, feeding at night on small animals and
birds, leaves and fruit. Lumholtz's Tree-kangaroo
(right) has forsaken the terrestrial habitat of
other kangaroos and taken to the trees. Evolution
has made its fore limbs more powerful, its hind
feet broader and shorter and its tail rounder in
comparison with plains kangaroos. Both the
Cuscus and the Tree-kangaroo are creatures of
the northern Queensland forests.

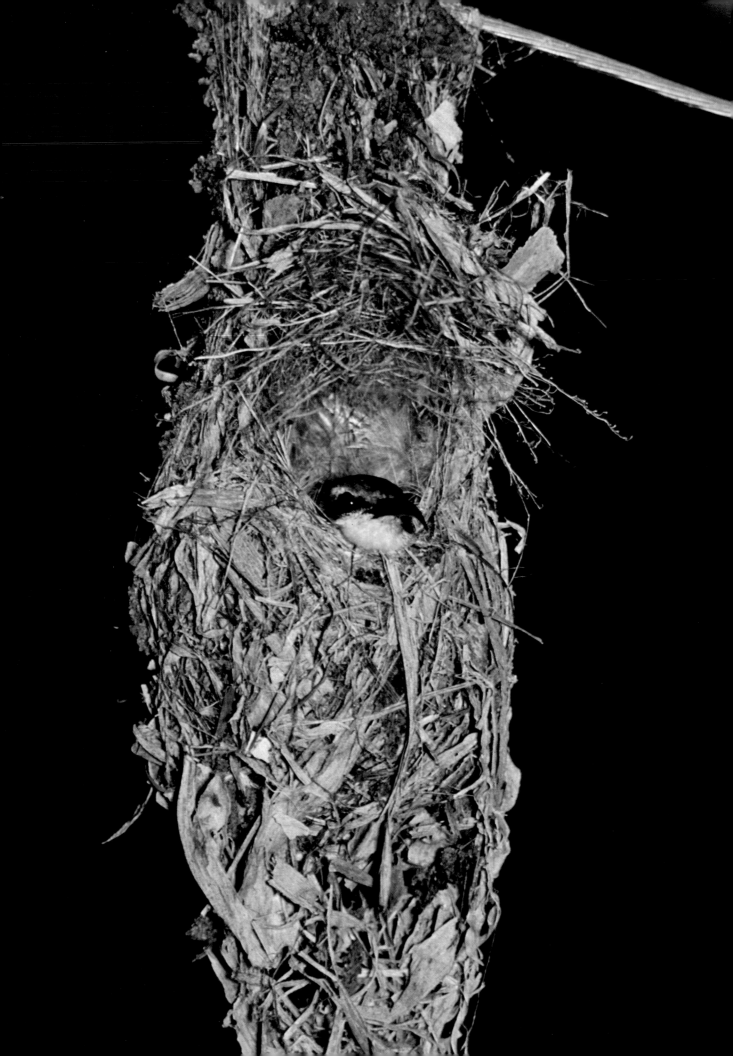

The small Yellow-breasted Sunbird is equipped with a long, thin, curving bill for nectar-feeding and has a humming-bird habit of hovering near flowers. Its curious nest of bark-fibre, grass and leaves bound with cobwebs is often suspended on rope or wire.

Index

Common names and scientific names of animals and birds in this book

Albatross, Wandering	*Diomedea exulans*	10
Ant, Indian (Weaver)	*Oecophylla smaragdina*	38
Bailer Shell	*Voluta aethiopia*	72
Bandicoot, Short-nosed	*Isoodon obesulus*	26
Bat, White Mastif	*Tadarida australis*	36
Bower-bird, Satin	*Ptilonorhynchus violaceus*	30
Bower-bird, Spotted	*Chlamydera maculata*	56
Brolga	*Grus rubicunda*	66, 67
Budgerigar	*Melopsittacus undulatus*	49
Cassowary	*Casuarius casuarius*	33
Clam, Giant	*Tridacna gigas*	72
Cockatoo, Sulphur-crested	*Kakatoe galerita*	44
Corella	*Kakatoe tenuirostris*	44
Cormorant, Black	*Phalacrocorax carbo*	10
Crab, Green Mud	*Scylla serrata*	73
Crocodile, Estuarine	*Crocodylus porosus*	65
Crocodile, Johnstone's	*Crocodylus johnstoni*	76
Cuscus	*Phalanger maculatus*	77
Dingo	*Canis familiaris*	58
Dragon, Boyd's Forest	*Goniocephalus boydii*	36
Duck, Whistle	*Dendrocygna eytoni*	62, 63, 65
Eagle, Wedge-tailed	*Aquila audax*	15
Echidna	*Tachyglossus aculeatus*	45
Emu	*Dromaius novae-hollandiae*	46, 47
Finch, Black-throated or Parson	*Poephila cincta*	57
Frogmouth, Tawny	*Podargus strigoides*	34
Galah	*Kakatoe roseicapilla*	43
Gannet, Australian	*Sula serrator*	12
Glider, Feathertail	*Acrobates pygmaeus*	28
Glider, Greater	*Schoinobates volans*	29
Glider, Squirrel	*Petaurus norfolcensis*	18, 28
Glider, Sugar	*Petaurus breviceps*	37
Goose, Cape Barren	*Cereopsis novae-hollandiae*	11
Goose, Magpie	*Anseranas selmipalmata*	62, 63
Gull, Silver	*Larus novae-hollandiae*	11
Harrier, Spotted	*Circus assimilis*	54
Jabiru	*Xenorhynchus asiaticus*	61

Kangaroo, Grey	*Macropus giganteus*	15, 24
Kangaroo, Red	*Megaleia rufa*	50, 51
Kestrel, Nankeen	*Falco cenchroides*	55
Kingfisher, Azure	*Alcyone azurea*	64
Koala	*Phascolarctos cinereus*	2, 22, 23
Kookaburra, Blue-winged	*Dacelo leachi*	26
Kookaburra, Laughing	*Dacelo gigas*	27
Lorikeet, Rainbow	*Trichoglossus molluccanus*	71
Lyrebird, Superb	*Menura superba*	34, 35
Mallee-fowl	*Leipoa ocellata*	48, 49
Numbat	*Myrmecobius fasciatus*	53
Owl, Barn	*Tyto alba*	16
Parrot, Red-browed Fig	*Opopsitta diopthalma macleayana*	76
Pelican	*Pelecanus conspicillatus*	68
Pigeon, Plumed or Spinifex	*Lophophaps plumifera*	52
Platypus	*Ornithorhyncus anatinus*	20, 21
Possum, Brush-tailed	*Hemibelideus lemuroides*	19
Possum, Ring-tailed	*Pseudocheirus peregrinus*	37
Potoroo	*Potorous tridactylus*	35
Python, Green	*Chrondropython viridis*	38
Rosella, Crimson	*Platycercus elegans*	16
Sealion, Australian	*Neophoca cinerea*	9
Sunbird, Yellow-fronted	*Cyrtostomus frenatus*	78
Swan, Black	*Cygnus atratus*	4
Tasmanian Devil	*Sarcophilus harrisii*	28
Tern, Sooty	*Sterna bergii*	74, 75
Tiger Cat	*Dasyurus maculatus*	40
Tree-frog, Two-colour or Dwarf	*Hyla bicolor*	39
Tree-kangaroo, Lumholtz's	*Dendrolagus lumholtzi*	77
Turtle, Loggerhead	*Caretta caretta*	73
Wallaby, Swamp	*Wallabia bicolor*	25
Wallaby, Yellow-footed Rock	*Petrogale xanthopus*	52
Wombat, Common	*Vombatus ursinus*	17
Wombat, Hairy-nosed	*Lasiorhinus latifrons*	57
Wren, White-winged	*Malurus cyanotus*	56

PHOTOGRAPHY

HANS AND JUDY BESTE: 16 (below); 34 (below); 35 (top); 43; 48; 49 (top); 49 (below); 53; 54; 56 (below); 66 (top); 66 (below); 76 (below). JOHN BROWNLIE: 25; 50; 51 (top); 51 (below). JOHN CARNEMOLLA: 11 (top); 15; 24 (below); 27; 28 (below Right); 47; 58; 67; 68; 73 (above); 74-75; 76 (top); 77 (below). DENSEY CLYNE: 36 (below); 38 (top); 38 (below). HARRY FRAUCA: 11 (below); 12; 16; 17; 18 (below); 19; 20 (below); 22; 24 (top); 26 (below); 28 (below Left); 29; 36 (top); 37 (top); 37 (below); 39; 44 (top); 45 (top); 45 (below); 46; 52 (top); 55; 64; 65 (top); 72 (top). MICHAEL MORCOMBE: frontispiece; 4; 9; 20 (top); 23; 30; 35 (below); 40; 52; 77 (above). F. G. MYERS: 10 (top); 10 (below); 18 (top); 26 (top); 34 (top); 44 (below); 56; 57 (below); 65 (below); 71; 72 (below); 73 (below). ROBIN SMITH: 21; 57 (top); 61; 62-63; 78.

RIGBY LIMITED

Adelaide   Sydney   Melbourne   Perth   Brisbane

First published in 1975

National Library of Australia Registry Card Number and ISBN 0 85179 975 2

This book was designed and set in Australia and printed in Hong Kong

Copyright John Currey, O'Neil Pty Ltd